SO YOU THINK YOU CAN

KASHANA YARA WAPLES

Palmetto Publishing Group
Charleston, SC

So You Think You Can Juice
Copyright © 2020 by Kashana Yara Waples

First Edition

Printed in the United States

ISBN-13 978-1-64111-797-5
ISBN-10: 1-64111-797-4

Luke 1:45

And blessed is she that believed: for there shall be a performance of those things which were told her from the Lord.

MY JUICING JOURNEY

Juicing started at the age of eight years old for me. My grandma Thelma Jennings, who suffered from diabetes, heart failure, and arthritis, would take out her juicer daily. It was an Acme 5001 Juicerator. She would juice carrots, celery, apples, and sometimes grapes. She would say, "This juice really makes me feel better; the celery juice helps with reducing the swelling in my feet. I'll show you how to make your own." So when I came to visit, she did just that. I remember putting loads of fruits and veggies in that juicer and getting less than half a cup of juice. When she passed away the next year, my grandpa Anthony Jennings gave me the juicer.

The next month at Forrest Hill Elementary School, as fourth graders, we were asked to present something to the class that was valuable to us. I brought in my grandma's juicer. I brought in my favorite combination at the time: carrots and grapes. I was so excited that my grandma had taught me this and I could share it with my class. The presentation went well, and my classmates loved the juice, but the cleanup was too much to handle. Being nine years old with no real responsibility, I left the dirty juicer at school. That was the last time I saw or used that juicer.

My next encounter with a juicer was ten years later. My father, Artie Waples, was so assertive when he said, "Girl, get over here and drink this juice; it's good for you."

My father juiced kale, collard greens, parsley, and celery.

I would walk toward him with disgust and my eyes rolling in my head (just like my son does to me now). I yelled, "Dad, I'm not drinking that!"

My dad said, "Girl, you better sit down here and drink this juice."

It was awful! I said, "Dad, put an apple in it or something!"

He said, "Yara, you are sweet enough. Now, drink the juice."

I laughed and drank the juice. The energy I felt behind his blend blew my mind. Since that day, juicing history was made for me. I would not purchase my own juicer, and my father with his stingy self would not give me his Vitamix juicer.

So, throughout the years, I would just purchase fresh juices while walking in the mall or on vacation, until one day, about twelve years later, when my sister Robbin Pegues wanted something from me. I said, "Well, even swap—let me have your juicer." She gave me her Breville and taught me how to cut the cleanup time in half.

Robbin said, "Yara, just put a bag in the back so it can get all the pulp. Make sure you wash your fruit. And this part I know you will love: it's dishwasher safe."

I was sold immediately and was super thankful!

In 2010 I was working out with one of Camden's best trainers. He would work us to the bone. I mean, he built my endurance up within three months. His children ran laps around us as we would all pray to God that he only gave us ninety-nine jumping jacks that hour, instead of four hundred. Our classes were rough, and he didn't miss a beat, especially with Tina Harmon, Wally Hannah (Wallies Smoothies) and others, telling on anyone who cheated or missed a count. While working out, I felt like I wanted to throw up because I had the nerve to eat before his session.

An idea instantly popped in my head: "Girl, if you don't, juice." I started juicing before the workouts, which gave me the energy to get through, and I also juiced after the workout to hydrate and put back nutrients I lost while working out. My blends used to come from a small book from the flea market that my mom had bought for me a few years prior. I swear, every recipe in that small book tasted so good.

The yo-yo dieter and fake workout queen in me said, "Let me start a juice fast." This was in 2014. My hairdresser, Annagjid "Kee" Taylor (salon owner of Deeper Than Hair and CEO of Shear Genius Collection), would do a sixty-day juice fast every year. The juices looked amazing! I discussed this with my longtime friend Elton Custis, and he was down. Elton said to post it on Facebook. Next thing I know, Donald Custis, Michelle Perry, Zakiyyah Moore, and another friend of Elton's was on board. We completed a sixty-day juice fast! Oh my goodness, we did it. I was scared of the scale and never weighed myself, but my clothes were fitting right. My stomach was flat, my skin was amazing, and my energy was wonderful. We all lost weight, but we never did a sixty-day fast again until October 2019.

First Juicing experience in 2014
60 day challenge

In 2016, I was laid off from my program manager job. At this time, I saw a talent in a friend of mine. Boy, could he cook! I figured I would help build his business. I received my MBA in 2010, so I had the knowledge. He would do the cooking, and I would sell my juices to his customers. He had this one dedicated customer named Anthony McFadden (owner and professional trainer of Versatile Fitness in Westville, New Jersey), who would buy my juices (he was the only one) every time he would purchase the Ant Workout Wrap (it was my idea to name it after him because of his loyalty; this man bought a wrap every day). I was there day in and day out, testing my skills in business. My mom saw my talent and would ask, "Yara, why are you using your energy and time on that project when you have your own talent? Go out and get your own." We were in the heart of the hood, making people happy with fresh food and, of course, my juices. One day, that same friend that I helped build up told me, "Niggas aren't going to buy these juices." Boy, was he wrong. So I moved on and started another project that wasn't juice related.

I was not really into the "Juicing is life" concept yet, until one day, my girlfriends Tina Harmon (founder of Mixed Minds Book Club) and Sylvia Sanders (owner and lash extension specialist of Kiss My Lash Lounge) sat down to discuss cleansing. We would do the Beyoncé lemonade diet, work out together, and juice.

I guess my juices were so good that Sylvia and Tina posted the juices. Next thing I know, I'm started to receive calls left and right: "Please make me some juices; I will pay you." I said, "Pay me!" Wow, sure, OK! Tina juiced for a month, without eating, and not only was she glowing, but she also got a promotion. My girlfriend was fasting and didn't even realize how spiritual it was for her. Tina's intention was to help reduce her issues related to her irritable bowel syndrome. The juicing worked, and she received a promotion at her job too. She took several medications for IBS, and none of them worked, but juicing did. Sylvia lost so much weight from juicing that her family and friends started to call for juices, even from as far away as Delaware. At this point, I started posting on my personal IG and Facebook pages, and business started to pour in.

Pete Brown was my favorite juicing story of all times. Not only did Pete lose weight by juicing, but he changed his eating habits too. Pete stopped taking his blood pressure meds and believed in the power of juicing. Pete was healed—no more high blood pressure for him. Pete would call every week: "When can we meet?" Pete juiced for three months, five days at a time. Pete drank two juices per day and ate a healthy meal. He followed the instructions I provided with the juices better than I did. He started exercising and would rave about his officer uniform and how he needed to get a smaller size. He went on Facebook and did a small commercial about my juices. Next thing I knew, a few of his coworkers would call and place orders. I would provide juices to help keep his blood pressure down—juices (which you will see later in this book) like beet lemonade, watermelon mojito, cucumber lemonade, parsnip punch, natural eggnog, and a few others. After three months, Pete didn't need my juices anymore. Pete's eating habits completely changed! Pete would call from time to time just for a cleanse. Pete was consistent, and it showed.

I'm a poop-flow, intestine-lengths, bowel-movement type of girl. Yes, if you are drinking juices from me, I am going to need to know what color and shape your bowel movements are and how many times a day you are going. When Nick Smith started drinking my juices, I received a text from him in regard to his bowel movements.

Nick: Yara, why is my bowel movement red?

Me: Oh, I forgot to tell you the beet juice will turn your bowels and urine red.

Nick sent back a text with a rolling-eyes emoji.

After weeks of juicing, I would get random texts in regard to his bowel movements.

Nick: I have a new appreciation for the bathroom. What are you giving me? I pooped every color in the rainbow.

He loved the juices so much, he would call at least once a month: "I need more juices." I normally would provide pint-size juices to my clients, but Nick would purchase the quart-size jars.

Cleansing your bowels is very important. Otherwise the dead animals, fruits, or veggies will rot inside your stomach. Juicing is also good for removing intestinal worms. You must cleanse! Your intestines will hold on to food for months. Most diseases start in the gut, and a good cleanse at least twice a year is a great thing.

I can go on and on about my juice clients and their juice stories, but this one particular client inspired me to write this book. "Cherelle—no allergies" is how she is stored in my phone. My reason behind calling her and other clients "no allergies" was because when they called to get their juices, I needed to know their goals, whether they were on any medication that interfered with fresh produce and herbs, and what allergies they had to food. Their questions were, "How much, and do you have a menu?" Yes, I do have a menu, but I never allowed my juice clients to have a choice on what I made them. My main concern was if they had allergies to fruit, veggies, or herbs and their goals. My clients never had to worry about the taste, because I consistently get texts and phone calls raving about how great tasting my juices are. One client asked if I would put sugar in my juices. My response was, never! Apples are my secret. I would also compare my juices to the way my clients drink their wine. If they liked a dry red wine like I did, that would help me determine how many apples I need to put in the juices, or if I needed to put in any apples at all. Otherwise, I would use apples, pears, oranges, or pineapples to sweeten the juices I make.

Furthermore, if they chose the juices they wanted from my menu, they would not be able to experience all my juice flavors. While juicing, I'm at my happiest because I love to juice, and I love experimenting with various fruits, herbs, and vegetables. In my opinion, you can follow a recipe book, but it's up to your taste buds to tell you the measurements. I would get suggestions to measure out my juices and write down how many of this and that goes in each jar. My response was, I can't, because all fruits and vegetables comes in various shapes and sizes. I know the ingredients to make each jar perfect and what fruit or vegetable over-powers what. For instance, light fruits like watermelons will not stand out in a juice if you add citrus or rooted veggies. Use half of a peeled citrus fruit to give the juice a splash of a citrus taste. Use the apple to enhance the taste of the watermelon. If you want to follow my recipes and add mint for the watermelon mojito, use up to twelve leaves for a sixteen-ounce jar, but again experiment with the flavors of the produce you buy. Pineapples, beets, and carrots are very strong in taste, so to taste citrus, ginger, mint, or turmeric, you may need to add a whole lemon, a handful of mint, or more than a thumb of ginger. Fresh turmeric is very overpowering and will take over the taste of any juice if you put too much in, so use it sparingly.

I would give my clients up to six different flavors with each ten-jar cleanse. I figured if I didn't like drinking the same thing every day, they wouldn't either. Plus, with trial and error, I knew what juices last the longest in mason jars. For instance, any green juice blends, besides celery, would only last fresh in a mason jar for three to four days. Plain celery juice could last up to six days. Watermelons and other melon blends last for five days. Any root-blended juices could last up to eight days; roots include carrots, parsnips, beets, and golden beets. Oranges, pineapples, and apples can last up to eight days. When fresh produce items are juiced, they start to lose their vitamin and nutrient values as soon as the juices hit the air, so it's very important to close the juices up immediately in a glass container with an airtight lid. Juices can stay fresher if you wrap them in foil and place them in the back of a refrigerator. I would also inform my juice clients to drink the juices within two hours of opening their jars. Some clients would tell me they opened them all, tasted them, and put them back in the refrigerator and switch the jars out to a plastic bottle. My response would be to please keep them sealed in the jars until it's time to drink them. This method would help to lock in the freshness of each juice inside the jar. As far as changing containers, the juice will lose important nutrients your body needs. I also would explain to them why I use mason jars versus plastic containers. I would ask, "Have you ever drunk water out of a glass container or stored food in a glass container? Well, the water tastes so crisp and the food remains as tasty as it did the day you cooked it when storing it in glass. Not to mention, the environment would thank you later."

So getting back to Cherelle—she completed her cleanse between May and December of 2018. During this time, she achieved her weight loss goal and a promotion. I always felt juicing was more spiritual than anything else. Giving up food is huge, and to give it up for one, two, or even three meals a day is considered fasting. Honestly, you need the Lord to get through this journey. It takes discipline, and it's not easy at times. Imagine not chewing for days.

One day in December, Cherelle posted on her Instagram status that she was "securing her bag!" It appeared everyone in the comments section knew exactly what she meant but me. So I sent Cherelle a text message.

Me: What do you mean, securing your bag?

Cherelle: It's funny you texted me. I had a dream about you last night.

She never told me what the dream was about, but she went on to say that she was promoted to director at her job, she closed on a home, and she would be buying another rehab home. I was so happy for her.

Cherelle: I will not read a juice book until you write one.

This message was mind blowing to me; I was in the middle of writing another book, but why not let juicing be my first book to release? Honestly, I had no clue on how to publish, but in due time I would contact my childhood friend Kenny Mahan (author of *Minnesota Baps*).

My most difficult juice client was: my girlfriend Yogie, who called me back in 2018 to tell me about a juicer she had bought. She tried juicing her own juices and gave up, after juicing 6 pint size jars. The next year she had a birthday party, and as a gift, I decided to help my friend and give her a juice cleanse for her birthday. I get a text: "Hmmmmm, these juices are not filling me up but OMG this green goodness is so good." Two months later: "I'll pay anything, I need to lose 20 pounds by April 1st." So I rushed over to her job in Philadelphia the next day so she could start her juice journey. Two days later, I get a text from Yogie: "I meant to tell you, I don't like sweet potatoes!" (along with the throwing-up emoji). She went on, saying: "It tastes like dirt, I hate sweet potatoes [followed by crying and laughing emojis]. I am going to chase it down with that dandelion tea, you suggested." I responded: "Girl, you know I wash and peel my sweet potatoes." Next text: "OMG YARA, I'm starving and this celery one" with several throwing-up emojis this time.

The next day, Yogie texted again: "I'm down 5 pounds, I love the Red Robbin, and OMG as soon as I get to the gym, the celery juice wants to come through, LORDT!" The next day: No words, just a text with a picture of carrots plus more throwing-up emojis. I respond: "OK, so I know now no carrots, sweet potatoes, or celery." She replies: "No we can keep the celery, I like the poop, lol." The next week, she goes on Facebook and Instagram, telling everyone she is about to juice all these fruits and veggies. Two hours later, she's telling the public: "I am not in the juicing business, Yara can have this, I save lives but not this way, it's too much work and her feet hurt." Well, for the next two weeks, I received texts like this. She lost her twenty pounds and has a new appreciation for the fruits and veggies, she didn't like.

Juicing certain produce can be harmful to some people, and my juice clients and I learned the hard way. Taking blood thinners and blood pressure medication while juicing greens can harm you. I had a juice client who had a massive heart attack after drinking green blended juices for over a month. He reported his doctor advised him that his vitamin K levels were too high. The doctor said to him that he could eat his greens but he could not juice greens while taking blood thinner or high blood pressure meds. That's when I learned to ask my juice clients about the meds they take before they get into this juice journey. I put a disclaimer on the literature I provided, stating that I am not a doctor and to please advise your doctor before detoxing through natural juices.

Time went on, and my juice clients grew to those from New Jersey, Philadelphia, and Delaware and as far away as New York.

TESTIMONIES FROM JUICE CLIENTS

*check out www.juicecapitol.co

DAILY JUICE PICTURES AND FACTS

Check out @juicing_is_life
on Instagram
and
Juice Capitol
on Youtube, Facebook, Pinterest
and Twitter

Spiced Orange Juice

Oranges
Ginger
Turmeric

@Juicing_is_life

Carrot Plus
Carrot
Turmeric
Ginger

JUICING INSTRUCTIONS

There are three ways to juice: the morning routine, the cleanse, or the fast. All three ways will give you the energy you need and increase blood levels of antioxidants, vitamins, and minerals. Juicing also helps to push out or reduce inflammation in the body. As you read each recipe on the upcoming pages, you will see which recipes fit your needs.

The Morning Routine

I call this "the morning routine" because this goes along with brushing your teeth and washing your body and face. You should not miss this routine. It's very important, and it is most important to do this as soon as you rise or before you put anything else in your mouth to chew or to drink. You are fasting for up to eight hours each night, allowing your body, mind, and organs to rest. Once you wake up, you don't want to add any unnecessary pressure to the brain. Let your brain focus on other important things like stepping out of bed, thanking the Lord for another day, and walking your behind to the bathroom to brush the morning breath away (or, for those who have no teeth, *rinse* the morning breath away). If you are at your ideal weight but don't get enough fruits, veggies, minerals, or vitamins in daily, I suggest you drink one juice per day. Juicing before breakfast or for breakfast will give you the energy you need to fuel your day. This will also give you the correct size and width of a bowel movement the very next day. I suggest a sixteen-ounce glass of fresh juice.

The Cleanse

I call this "the cleanse" because you are not totally going without food. The length of time you are going without food is helping to detox or/and cleanse your liver, kidney, blood vessels, brain, nerve cells, skin cells, hair cells, teeth, pancreas, intestines, heart, eyes, gallbladder, colon, bladder, spleen, lungs, and bones. Did I leave anything out? Well, you get the picture. With the cleanse, you are fasting with juice up to sixteen hours, so what you put in your body during and after your last juice is very important. During the cleansing, you will drink a sixteen-ounce glass of juice for breakfast. You can drink water, plain sea moss gel, dandelion tea, and water. I suggest these three drinks because they help suppress the appetite, and these drinks are not harsh on your stomach. After you drink your last juice, typically after lunch, wait at least two to three hours before eating. Drink up to eight glasses of water per day to help the juices push out all the impurities you have been putting in your body. Some like to eat lunch and drink the other juice for dinner; that is OK, too, as long as you drink your last juice on an empty stomach, meaning two to four hours after your last meal. Your meals during this cleanse should contain fresh raw fruits, fresh raw or cooked vegetables, fresh or dried herbs, nuts, nut butters, beans, coconut oil, olive oil, vinegar, and agave. I also suggest that if this is your first time doing so and you have a weight loss goal or have had a health scare, do the cleanse for at least one to three months for the best outcome. You can incorporate exercise if you want, but most people will achieve their goals without it. After one to three months of the cleanse, you can go down to the morning routine; then, do a cleanse at least once a month to maintain your weight or health issues.

The Fast

I call this "the fast" because you will be doing nothing but juicing. The same rules apply for the fast: no food; you can substitute a juice for a smoothie and drink dandelion tea, fresh fruit and vegetable sea moss smoothies, and water. If you need to sweeten your tea or smoothies, use agave. I am not too big on honey because it comes from an animal. If you prefer honey instead of agave, go for it. One to two months of the fast is sufficient. You can drop down to the cleanse, complete that for a month, and then drop down to the morning routine. With the fast, you will lose weight. Your skin will change; your organs inside will become new and start to heal, and whatever issues you had before the fast will be gone, or it will change the levels throughout your body in a good way. After you have completed the fast, you will not eat the same or drink the same as you have before. Please listen to your body! Your body will reject anything that's high in fat, alcohol, salt, sodium, and so forth. Again, listen to your body! You will experience headaches and stomach aches, and you may even break out. Listen to what is going on, and don't do it again, or you will be right back to square one. The first two to three days of the fast, you may experience headaches and diarrhea, and you may even become nauseous, but keep going; don't stop. This is your body trying to get rid of all the toxins within your body the best way it knows how.

The Cleanse

Breakfast

Lunch

Dinner

*during the cleanse, you can drink tea(I suggest "dandelion" because it suppresses your appetite) and water.

JUICING RECIPES AND BENEFITS

Watermelon Mojito

Watermelon, apple, mint, lime

Benefits may include promoting a healthy complexion and hair, increased energy, and overall lower weight. May help asthma prevention, growth of male's reproduction system, blood pressure, cancer, digestion, and regularity. Also may help with hydration, inflammation, muscle soreness, and skin. May increase sex drive.

1/8 watermelon (rind removed)

2 apples

1/2 cup fresh mint

1/2 lime (rind removed)

Spiced Orange Juice

Oranges, ginger, turmeric

Benefits may include helping metabolize carbohydrates, thanks to the natural sugar, vitamins, minerals, and enzymes naturally found in oranges. It's also essential for normal immune system function. Vitamin C is also an antioxidant that may have health benefits by protecting your cells from free-radical damage. This juice may reduce cholesterol levels, boost immunity, prevent cancer, detoxify the body, help the liver, support blood circulation, reduce high blood pressure, and relieve pain and stiffness.

5 oranges (rinds removed)

Thumb of ginger (size of your thumb)

Thumb of fresh turmeric (size of your thumb)

Nature's Egg-Not

Parsnip, pear, lime, ginger

Benefits may include helping bone matrix proteins, preventing bone loss, helping with type 2 diabetes, and improving blood sugar levels and insulin levels. This juice may improve cognitive function and is a big source of manganese.

5 parsnips

3 pears

1/2 lime (rind removed)

Thumb of ginger (size of your thumb)

Parsnip Punch

Parsnip, apple, pineapple, lime, ginger

Benefits may include the reduction of blood pressure and diabetes. May improve bowel health, heart, cancer. This drink is a diuretic and a great source of fiber and may also support kidney and spleen function.

5 parsnips

2 apples

1/4 pineapple (rind removed)

1/2 lime (rind removed)

Thumb of ginger (size of your thumb)

Hot Toddy

Grapefruit, orange, habanero

Benefits may include a combination of high contents of vitamins C and A and capsaicin; this may prevent cancer in a big way by inhibiting the growth of cancer cells (particularly prostate) and by preventing the negative effects of free radicals. This juice may also lower cholesterol, reduce blood pressure, and promote weight gain.

2 grapefruits (rinds removed)

5 oranges (rinds removed)

1/2 habanero (Please wear gloves while cutting, and don't rub eyes after.)

Tangy and Sweet

Persimmon, grapefruit

Benefits may include the improvement of lipid metabolism. May prevent the oxidation of low-density lipoprotein cholesterol (LDL-C), which halts the development of atherosclerosis. May protect from colorectal cancer; also may relieve symptoms of constipation and diarrhea. May prevent premature aging, improve vision, and improve metabolic activity and liver issues.

3 persimmons

2 grapefruit (rinds removed)

Lin-Ale

Pear, apple, ginger

Benefits may include measurable levels of iron that may boost red blood cell production in the body, therefore treating issues like anemia. This juice may help with osteoporosis, eliminate bleeding, regulate the nervous system, reduce inflammation, and lower the risk of cardiovascular problems associated with issues like hypertension.

3 pears

3 apples

Thumb of ginger

Cherrell

Jicama, carrots, pear, ginger

Benefits may include several nutrients, fiber, and antioxidants, which may provide health benefits, including improved digestion, weight loss, and a reduced risk of disease. This juice may increases the frequency of bowel movements, slow cognitive decline, brighten skin, and enhance mood.

1/2 jicama (peeled)

4 carrots

3 pears

Thumb of ginger

The Sunshine

Yellow pepper, pear, ginger

Benefits includes niacin, which is a B vitamin that may help keep your skin healthy. The vitamins in this juice may help your nerves work normally and may help to keep your digestive system working the way it's supposed to. This juice may help turn the food you eat into usable energy as well.

2 yellow peppers

4 pears

Thumb of ginger

Seductive Syl

Apple, spinach, lemon, ginger

Benefits may include preventing anemia, relieving rheumatoid arthritis, maintaining alkaline levels, curing bleeding gums and cataracts, and fighting osteoporosis. This juice also is high in antioxidants, which may fight cancer cells, strengthen hair and skin, and combat stomach problems and high blood pressure. This juice may be great for pregnant women as well.

4 apples

3 cups fresh spinach

1/4 lemon (rind removed)

Thumb of ginger

Mother Nature

Jicama, mint, cucumber, apple

Benefits may include alkalizing of the blood. Contains high antioxidant and anti-inflammatory properties that maybe helpful for relieving breathlessness and asthma. This juice may help reduce deficiency problems that result in easy bruising and swelling.

1/2 jicama (peeled)

1/2 cup fresh mint

1 cucumber

2 apples

Green Goddess

Lettuce, ,zucchini, orange, apple, lemon

Benefits may include healing properties for flavonoids, which may work incredibly to help pain and stiffness in the entire body. It also may naturally cure arthritis, prevent ulcers, beat inflammation, protect your blood vessels, and help with long-term weight loss.

2 zucchini

12 romaine lettuce leaves

2 oranges (rinds removed)

4 apples

1/4 lemon (rind removed)

Cantaloupe-Strawberry Lemonade

Cantaloupe, strawberry, apple, lemon, ginger

Benefits may include regulating menstrual flow and preventing menstrual cramps in women. It considerably reduces flow and blood clotting, inducing menstruation. This juice may promote the supply of oxygen to the brain, making one feel relaxed and focused. It contains superoxide dismutase, a compound that combats stress and calms anxiety. It may soothe the nervous system, preventing sleeping disorders. It also may prevent cell death caused by oxidative stress.

1/4 Cantaloupe (seeds and rind removed)

15 strawberries (stems removed)

2 apples

1/2 lemon (rind removed)

Thumb of ginger

The Carrot Cleanse

Carrots, lime, lemon, ginger, turmeric

Benefits may include improving cognitive function and reducing the risk of age-related memory problems and dementia. Oxidative stress is linked to brain cell damage and occurs when brain and nerve cells can't regenerate. This weakens nerve signaling and reduces cognitive function. However, this juice may strengthen brain function and improve memory.

10 carrots

1/2 lime (rind removed)

1/3 lemon

Thumb of ginger

Thumb of turmeric

Strawberry Basil Cocktail

Strawberries, basil, apples, limes

Benefits may include promoting tissue strength and enhancing the healing process of the body. This juice may boost collagen production, which keeps your skin young and healthy and prevents skin tearing and weakening of bones. The high manganese content, on the other hand, supports collagen production and may help the body to heal faster.

20 strawberries (stems removed)

1/4 cup basil

4 apples

1/2 lime (rind removed)

Strawberry-Watermelon Mojito

Strawberries, watermelon, apple, lime, mint

Benefits may include a source of phytonutrients. These nutrients may help in preventing inflammatory diseases such as asthma and arthritis. So make sure you consume this juice regularly to keep these problems at bay. Great for men's health and may improve sex drive. Also great for blood sugar control.

15 strawberries (stems removed)

1/8 watermelon (rind removed)

2 apples

1/2 lime (rind removed)

1/2 cup fresh mint

Grapefruit Mojito

Grapefruit, apples, mint

Benefits may include appetite control and weight loss. May improve heart health and may help with your immune system. This juice also has powerful antioxidants, which may help to reduce kidney stones and prevent insulin resistance and diabetes.

5 grapefruits

3 apples

1/2 cup fresh mint

The Winter's Cold Cure

Pineapple, orange, apple, garlic, ginger, turmeric

Benefits may include improvement of cold and flu symptoms. This drink may also increase blood flow. High in allicin, which may help stimulate circulation and blood flow to sexual organs in both men and women. This juice may even be helpful to tone your sagging breasts.

1/4 pineapple (rind removed)

3 oranges (rinds removed)

2 apples

4 fresh garlic cloves

2 thumb of ginger

2 thumb of turmeric

The Gimlet

Cucumber, basil, lemon, apple

Benefits may include easing of inflammation and joint pain. This juice may help to tackle stress, anxiety, sore throats, and coughs. This juice may also lower risks of heart disease, rheumatoid arthritis, and inflammatory bowel conditions.

1 cucumber

1/4 cup basil

1/4 lemon

3 apples

Watermelon Basil Smash

Watermelon, basil, apple, lime

Benefits may include prevention of asthma, blood pressure, inflammation, cancer, and muscle soreness. May help with hydration, skin, digestion, and regularity. This juice may help with men's health and sex drive. May also be good for fighting depression and managing diabetes. May support liver functions, promote healthy gut, and help detoxify the body.

1/8 watermelon (rind removed)

1/4 basil

2 apples

1/2 lime (rind removed)

Bloody Mary

Tomatoes, jalapeño, lemon, apples

Benefits may include the prevention of high cholesterol. It is rich in fiber, which helps in breaking down LDL, or bad cholesterol, in the body. It also has niacin, or vitamin B3, which is known for stabilizing cholesterol.

7 Roma tomatoes

1/2 jalapeño

1 lemon (rind removed)

3 apples

Sexy Tina

Red pepper, orange, green apple

Benefits may include fiber, protein, and iron. This juice provides protection to your cells that may reduce your risk of heart disease, cancer, and arthritis. This juice may be the cure for thinning hair, weight loss, cholesterol levels, type 2 diabetes, strokes, high blood pressure, and intestinal peristalsis. May help in eliminating waste from the body.

1 red bell pepper

3 oranges (rinds removed)

2 Granny Smith apples

Starburst

Pineapples, yellow pepper, ginger, apple

Benefits may include eye health, like improvements to visual impairments such as macular degeneration and cataracts, the main causes of which are old age and infections. This juice may also help to speed up recovery after surgery and strenuous exercise. May also aid in mental health, stress, and skin, hair, and nail growth. Good for vaginal health.

1/4 pineapple (rind removed)

2 yellow peppers

Thumb of ginger

3 apples

Orange Paradise

Oranges, apple, cantaloupe, papaya, ginger

Benefits may include improvement for lung health. The nutrients present in cantaloupe provide a synergistic combination, which may help to recover from nicotine withdrawal in people who are trying to quit smoking. This juice may also replenish the body from depleted vitamin A in a smoker.

1/4 cantaloupe (seeds and rind removed)

3 apples

3 oranges (rinds removed)

1/2 papaya or 1 minipapaya (seeds and rind removed)

Thumb of ginger

Melon Mojito

Honeydew, apple, mint, lime

Benefits may include vitamin C, which acts as an antioxidant in blood and cells, plays a role in boosting immunity, and assists in collagen production, making it an important in anti-aging. This juice may also be a good source of potassium and has the potential to reduce blood pressure. May support weight loss and help fight water retention by flushing out toxins and salts.

1/4 honeydew (seeds and rind removed)

3 apples

1/2 cup fresh mint

1 lime (rind removed)

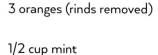

Orange Mojito

Oranges, mint, apple, lime

Benefits may include an overall boost in resistance due to the vitamin C content and may also stimulate the salivary glands, thus aiding digestion. May help lower cholesterol, prevent skin damage, build up immune system, and improve irritable bowel syndrome. May decrease breastfeeding pain while increasing breast milk flow. This juice may also aid in fertility.

3 oranges (rinds removed)

1/2 cup mint

4 apples

1 lime (rind removed)

Crush

Cantaloupe, mint, apple, lime

Benefits may include fighting kidney disease. This juice may be the key to pre-serving kidney function. This juice also contains myoinositol, a lipid that helps with anxiety, insomnia, and hardening of the arteries. This juice contains the greatest amount of digestive enzymes, which may aid in protection from damaging free radicals to all parts of the body. Greatest choice for eyesight health.

1/4 cantaloupe (seeds and rind removed)

1/2 cup mint

4 apples

1 lime (rind removed)

Mean Green

Celery, ginger, cucumber, fennel, squash, parsley, lemon, apple

Benefits may include all-day energy. This juice alkalizes the body and gives pH balance. May delay aging, improve gut health, enhance detoxification, support a healthy immune system, and help with colds, brittle nails, hair loss, bags under the eyes, and weight loss. Rich in chlorophyll, amino acids, and antioxidants, which clean the liver and blood and fight viruses and diseases. May also improve detoxification and decrease inflammation.

4 celery branches

1 thumb of ginger

1 cucumber

1/2 cup fennel

1 squash

1/2 cup parsley

1 lemon (rind removed)

6 apples

Golden Punch

Golden beet, pineapple, turmeric, ginger, apple, and carrot

Benefits may include aiding in weight loss and boosting longevity and sex drive. Natural anti-inflammatory compound. May increase the antioxidant capacity of the body. The juice may boost brain-derived neurotrophic factor, which is linked to improved brain function and a lower risk of brain diseases. May decrease high blood pressure, anemia, and liver issues.

2 golden beets (skins removed)

1/4 pineapple (rind removed)

1 thumb turmeric

1 thumb ginger

4 apples

4 carrots (skins removed)

Beet Lemonade

Beets, green apples, lemon, and ginger

Benefits may include the ability to lower blood pressure, prevent cancer, cleanse the liver, treat anemia, increase stamina, and boost the libido. May prevent macular degeneration, improve blood circulation, aid in skin care, prevent cataracts, build immunity, and improve respiratory problems.

2 beets (skins removed)

5 apples

1 lemon (rind removed)

2 thumbs of ginger

Tropical Green

Pineapple, apple, lime, kale, cucumber, parsley, and green pepper

Benefits may include fighting against stomach infections, constipation, coughs, colds, flu, indigestion, arthritis, and joint pain. May aid in teeth/gum health and skin hydration. May remove dead cells from skin. Also, may reduce sugar/fat cravings. May remove intestinal worms and aid with eyesight and sinusitis. May help to cure constipation and irregular bowel movements. May aid with weight loss, sore throat, and bronchitis.

1/4 pineapple (rind removed)

3 apples

1 lime (rind removed)

4 kale leaves

1 cucumber

1/2 cup parsley

1 green pepper

Valley Green

Kale, celery, and apple

Benefits may include promoting healthy skin and hair and digestion, and protecting against heart disease, cancer, and diabetes. When you are looking for powdered chlorophyll to add into your diet, look no more. This juice contains all the chlorophyll you need in one day. Skip the cow, and get all your protein in this juice.

12 kale leaves

1 celery stalk

7 apples

Celery Juice

Celery

Benefits may include hydration and a major way to alkalize the gut. Celery juices purify the bloodstream and enhance weight loss and are a natural laxative. Also, if you suffer from IBS, eczema, Crohn's disease, or colon cancer, this may be the best juice for it. This juice may have you regular within one day. May decrease high blood pressure, anemia, and liver issues.

2 celery stalks

Cucumber Lemonade

Cucumber, lemon, apple, and ginger

Benefits include aiding in skin health, the renal system, and digestion. Reduces inflammation. Aids in removal of intestinal worms. May lower blood pressure and promote weight loss. Maintains electrolyte balance and aids in diabetes. Helps with shiny hair and with hair that is falling out. Helps with joint pain and the nervous system, Alzheimer's, cancer, and bad breath. Relieves constipation. This juice also hydrates and is best for a hangover.

1 cucumber

1/4 lemon (rind removed)

4 apples

1/2 thumb of ginger

Cucumber Mojito

Cucumber, mint, lime, apple

Benefits include improving digestion, fighting infections, helping with weight loss, lowering blood sugar, reducing heart disease, preventing cancer, and reducing inflammation. This juice also enhances immunity, boosts iron absorption, and prevents kidney stones and disease. This juice also hydrates and is best for a hangover.

1 cucumber

1/2 cup mint

1/2 lime (rind removed)

4 apples

Red Paradise

Beets, pineapple, apple, ginger

Benefits include weight loss. Promotes fiber and good bacteria (the kind that women look for in yogurt), so, yes, this juice is good for the vagina. This juice also protects the lining of the stomach and lowers blood pressure, cholesterol, and the risk of diabetes. This juice also contains compounds that help fight asthma and promote mental health. Yes, this is a "feel-good" juice.

2 beets (skin removed)

1/2 pineapple (rind removed)

3 apples

2 thumbs of ginger

Apple Detox

Apple, lemon, ginger

Benefits include the treatment of indigestion, constipation, dental problems, throat infections, fever, internal bleeding, rheumatism, burns, obesity, respiratory disorders, cholera, and high blood pressure, while also benefiting your hair and skin. Helps strengthen your immune system and cleanse your stomach and is considered a blood purifier.

6 apples

Lemon (rind removed)

2 thumbs ginger

Apple Detox 2

Apple, lemon, fennel, ginger

Benefits includes boosting your digestive powers, keeping anemia away, protecting joints, and promoting healthy eyes. It's a natural way to stimulate breast milk for nursing mothers and helps to keep bacteria away and fight sore throat and bad breath. This juice is supersoothing on the tummy, which may be because it contains antioxidants—quercetin and rutin—which encourage more digestive juices in the stomach, making it easier for your body to break down and absorb as many nutrients as possible from digested food. The juice contains high amounts of fiber and folate, which not only help improve colon function, but also help combat cancer-causing free radicals and toxins in the gastrointestinal tract.

6 apples

Lemon (rind removed)

2 thumbs ginger

1/2 cup fennel

Purple Haze

Purple sweet potato, pineapple, apple, lemon, lime, ginger

Benefits include great endurance for athletes and ultrarunners. Helps to lower and regulate blood pressure. Helpful in managing diabetes, gout, and inflammation. Prevents blood clots. Aids in weight loss and cancer fighting, and purple sweet potato root has antibacterial properties that destroy bacteria or suppress their growth and ability to reproduce with E. coli, salmonella, Proteus, and *Vibrio parahaemolyticus.*

2 purple sweet potatoes (skins removed)

1/4 pineapple (rind removed)

2 apples

1/2 lemon (rind removed)

1 lime (rind removed)

2 thumbs ginger

Purple Star

Purple cabbage, pineapple, apple, ginger

Benefits includes preventing cancer, supporting eye health, promoting weight loss, enhancing and supporting a youthful look, managing ulcers, and supporting the immune system. Other benefits includes protecting against Alzheimer's disease, increasing bone mineral density, boosting metabolism, filtering the blood, and managing hypertension.

1/2 cup purple cabbage

1/4 pineapple (rind removed)

4 apples

1 thumb ginger

Carrot Plus

Carrot, turmeric, ginger

Benefits include improving the appearance of your skin, especially if you have a history of skin problems, such as rashes or psoriasis. This juice strengthens brain function and improves memory. It also improves cholesterol levels and reduces the risk of heart disease, leukemia, prostate cancer, and strokes. Lastly, carrot juice strengthens the immune system, strengthens vision, and aids in weight loss.

7 carrots (skin removed)

2 thumbs turmeric

2 thumbs ginger

Sweet Potato Punch

Sweet potato, pineapple, apple, carrot, lime, turmeric, ginger

Benefits include stabilizing blood sugar and improving bones, teeth, skin, nerves, and thyroid gland health. Cleans the gastrointestinal tract and reduces the possibility of ulcers, heartburn, and acidity. Stabilizes levels of homocysteine (anti-stress mineral that accelerates the healing of wounds). This juice provides iron and provides relief with muscle cramping.

2 sweet potatoes (skins removed)

1/4 pineapple (rind removed)

3 apples

4 carrots (skins removed)

1 lime (rind removed)

2 thumbs turmeric

2 thumbs ginger

Strawberry Pineapple Lemonade

Strawberry, pineapple, apple, lemon, ginger

Benefits include promoting bone health, suppressing the appetite, and lowering or preventing high blood pressure. Reduces gut inflammation and inflammatory bowel disease. Promotes vaginal health and widens the arteries, which prevents plaque buildup.

20 strawberries (stems removed)

1/4 pineapple (rind removed)

2 apples

1/2 lemon (rind removed)

1 thumb ginger

Roots

Beets, carrots, sweet potato, apple, turmeric, ginger

Benefits include boosting stamina to help you exercise longer, improving blood flow, and helping to lower blood pressure. This juice can help cure and may prevent the bacteria that live in the stomach and cause stomach ulcers and heartburn. May help cure high blood pressure and anemia.

2 beets (skins removed)

4 carrots (skins removed)

2 sweet potatoes (skins removed)

5 apples

2 thumbs turmeric

2 thumbs ginger

The Beverage

Pineapple, carrot, ginger, turmeric

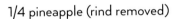

Benefits include strengthening your immune system. May help your body fight off infections. Add this juice to your daily diet, and maintain your physical health. This juice contains antioxidants, which may help your body fight free radicals, cell damage, and inflammation. Great for blood pressure, diabetes, anemia, and liver disease. Good for nursing moms.

1/4 pineapple (rind removed)

4 carrots (skins removed)

2 thumbs ginger

1 thumb turmeric

Koi So Cool

Orange, apple, lemon, ginger

Containing the body's primary water-soluble antioxidant, this juice is packed with vitamin C, which prevents damage to cells and reduces inflammation. It lowers the risk of chronic illnesses such as heart disease and arthritis. Great for nursing moms and fertility.

3 oranges (rinds removed)

3 apples

1/2 lemon (rind removed)

1 thumb ginger

Grandma Thelma

Carrot, celery, apple, grapes

Benefits include reducing the risk of blood clots, reducing low-density lipoprotein (LDL, or "bad") cholesterol, preventing damage to blood vessels in your heart, and helping maintain a healthy blood pressure. Helps with liver issues, diabetes, eczema, breastfeeding, and cardiovascular disease.

4 carrots (skins removed)

7 celery branches

3 cups grapes

5 apples

Father R. J.

Kale, collard greens, parsley, spinach

This is a natural diuretic, which helps to eliminate excess fluid without depleting the body of potassium. This juice is also an excellent source of vitamin A, vitamin C, and calcium and is a rich source of vitamin K and a good source of iron, vitamin B6, and magnesium.

7 kale leaves

7 collard leaves

1 cup parsley

3 cups spinach

Versatile Fitness Blast

Pineapple, grapefruit, orange, lemon, ginger

Benefits include promoting appetite control, aiding in weight loss, and helping burn belly fat. This drink is great for preworkout and postworkout. This juice also boosts your metabolism and contains needed daily fiber. Great for nursing moms and fertility.

1/2 pineapple (rind removed)

2 grapefruit (rinds removed)

3 oranges (rinds removed)

1 lemon (rind removed)

2 thumbs ginger

Sweet Green

Apple, cucumber, pineapple, green pepper, lime, ginger

Contains a high amount of vitamin B6, which is one of the most vital nutrients for our bodies. From improving our immunity to keeping our nervous system up, it can regulate a number of bodily functions effectively. Great for before and after a workout. Improves cognitive function and glowing skin and helps to alkalize the body.

5 apples

1/4 pineapple (rind removed)

1 cucumber

1 green pepper

1 lime (rind removed)

1 thumb ginger

T. E.'s Turmeric Toddy

Pineapple, lime, ginger, turmeric

Benefits include healthy digestion. Potent anti-inflammatory and antioxidant, which may help with symptoms of depression, cancer, Alzheimer's, obesity, and arthritis. Also relieves premenstrual tension and supports healthy joints, cholesterol levels, and normal blood sugar levels. This juice can be more effective than Tylenol.

1 whole pineapple (rind removed)

2 limes (rinds removed)

2 thumbs ginger

2 thumbs turmeric

Green Giant

Basil, parsley, zucchini, green pepper, lemon, green apple, spinach, and ginger

Benefits include high doses of protein and fiber. Boosts energy and is very rich in phytochemicals that get rid of excess glucose and sodium in the system. This juice will help to lower blood sugar levels, slow down aging, and improve thyroid and adrenal functions. It also protects against oxidation and inflammation.

1/4 cup basil leaves

1/2 cup parsley

2 zucchini

1 green pepper

1/2 lemon

2 cups spinach

5 apples

1 thumb lemon

Lucky Charms

Kale, collards, cucumber, fennel, zucchini, green pepper, and spinach

Benefits include and aids in weight loss, fatigue, impotence, kidney function, and eye health. Also helps with menopause, hair loss, liver functions, and thyroid issues. Forget that chlorophyll tablet, and drink this juice; it's full of all the chlorophyll you need. *Warning: This juice is very strong, and if you are on blood thinners, do not consume this juice.*

7 kale leaves

7 collard leaves

1/4 cup fennel

2 zucchini

1 green pepper

2 cups spinach

Robbin's Nest

Red pepper, lemon, apple, and ginger

Benefits include artery cleansing, circulation repair, and reduction of high blood pressure. Helps with eye health and skin problems. This juice helps with problems in hair loss and arthritis, and it contains more vitamin C and vitamin A than most juices. This juice has the potential to burn more calories.

1 red pepper

1/2 lemon (rind removed)

4 apples

1 thumb of ginger

Greenade

Kale, celery, fennel, apple, lemon, ginger

Reduces water retention, and helps with constipation, indigestion, and bloating. This juice can also be great for acne, and it purifies the blood. This juice has a significant amount of fiber, which decreases the risk of heart disease, and it helps reduce the total amount of cholesterol in the blood.

7 kale leaves

5 celery branches

1/2 cup fennel

6 apples

1 lemon (rind removed)

1 thumb ginger

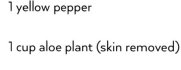

Island Sun

Yellow pepper, aloe, apple, lime, ginger

Benefits include digestive help. Treats constipation, psoriasis, and acne. Treats canker sores, lowers blood sugar, and improves skin and prevents wrinkles. Great for liver issues, diabetes, nursing moms, Crohn's disease, and weight loss. My suggestion is to take the aloe in this recipe and use it has a hair gel, leave-in conditioner, and scalp moisturizer. Do this three times a week for six months, and watch the change in your hair.

1 yellow pepper

1 cup aloe plant (skin removed)

5 apples

1 lime (rind removed)

1 thumb ginger

D. Brodie Green

Canary melon, cucumber, apple, lime, ginger

This is an excellent source of fiber, which can lower the rate of heart disease, diabetes, obesity, and high blood pressure. This juice also aids in healing before and after surgery. Great for a hangover, liver disease, and removal of belly fat and parasites and worms within the stomach area.

1/2 canary melon (rind removed)

1 cucumber

3 apples

1 lime (rind removed)

1 thumb ginger

Green Mojito

Cucumber, zucchini, apple, lime, mint

Benefits include a good amount of potassium, 295 milligrams per cup. This juice is also high in the antioxidant vitamin C, which may help the lining of your blood cells function better, lowering blood pressure and protecting against clogged arteries.

1 cucumber

1 zucchini

3 apples

1 lime (rind removed)

1/2 cup mint

Yara Juice

Cantaloupe, apple, ginger

Boosts immunity by stimulating the white blood cells in the body. This juice is very beneficial to the heart, as it carries blood thinners, and the vitamin C prevents hardening of the arties. Promotes healthy weight management, lower cholesterol, and bowel function. Helps with diabetes.

1 cantaloupe (rind removed)

4 apples

2 thumbs ginger

Jesus Juice

Pear, carrot, apple, ginger

Benefits include regulating bowel movements, giving a mild laxative effect, and working as a diuretic. Great cholesterol-lowering juice. It also helps tone the intestines and eliminate waste. Lowers risk of heart disease and diabetes. Helps with weight loss. Helps to bring forth more breast milk for nursing moms.

2 pears

2 apples

4 carrots (skins removed)

1 thumb ginger

Gangsta Green

Orange, carrot, apple, cucumber, turmeric

Benefits include weight loss; this is a great cholesterol-lowering juice. It also eases heartburn, stomach, and ulcers. Cures headaches, diabetes, and bad breath. Helps to bring forth more breast milk for nursing moms.

3 oranges

2 apples

1/2 cucumber

4 carrots (skins removed)

2 thumbs turmeric

Watermelon Blast

Watermelon, peaches, lemon, strawberries, ginger

Benefits include aiding in digestion, protecting skin, and improving heart health. Juice is great for erectile disfunction. It also moisturizes the skin and hair. Helps with weight loss and renews and repairs tissue.

1/2 watermelon (rind removed)

2 peaches (pits removed)

12 strawberries (stems removed)

1/2 lemon (skin removed)

1 thumb ginger

Oh, Heck No

Bitter melon, celery, apple, green bell pepper

Benefits include reduction of blood sugar. Juice has cancer-fighting properties. Decreases cholesterol levels and weight loss. Juice contains an insulin like compound and is an inflammation fighter. Honestly, it's not the best-tasting juice, but if you drink daily, it may help reduce blood sugar more than any juice around.

2 bitter melons

2 apples

4 celery branches

1 green bell pepper

Hot Green

Jalapeno, lime, parsley, cucumber, celery, apple, fennel, kale

Benefits include pain relief and weight loss. Fights infections. Juice is high in fiber and antioxidants. Helps with intestinal gas, bloating, and loss of appetite. Helps with vaginal issues after menopause.

1 jalapeño

1 cucumber

4 apples

1 cup parsley

1/2 cup fennel

3 celery branches

4 kale branches

1 lime

Green Fantasy

Pineapple, honeydew, parsley, lemon, apple, ginger

Benefits include regulating bowel movements. Gives a mild laxative effect and works as a diuretic. This is a great cholesterol-lowering juice; it also helps tone the intestines and aids in the elimination of waste. Lowers risk of heart disease and diabetes. Aids in weight loss and helps to bring forth more breast milk for nursing moms.

1/4 pineapple (rind removed)

1/4 honeydew (rind removed)

1 cup fresh parsley

1/2 lemon

3 apples

1 thumb ginger

2 apples

4 carrots (skins removed)

1 thumb ginger

*Note: The recipes seen above can be juiced in a masticating Juicer or a Centrifugal Juicer. Fruits and veggies come in various shapes and sizes. The recipes above may be larger than eight ounces of juice, and it may even taste different each time you make it. Once you continue to juice and know what you prefer, juicing will become natural. If you love ginger, add three to four thumbs per recipe. If you want your juice sweet, add more apples, pears, or pineapples. Have fun! For more recipes, visit my Instagram page, @juicing_is_life.

JUICING TIPS

Apples

- Buy very firm apples; otherwise, your juice will be mushy and filled with pulp.

- Apples are the secret to a sweet juice; it can turn the strongest-tasting juice sweet.

- Green apples are great to use if you suffer from high blood pressure or diabetes.

- I suggest Granny Smith, Gala, Fuji, Honeycrisp, Cameo, or Red Delicious.

- Cut the stems off, or you will be drinking them.

- Don't forget to wash them with 1/2 teaspoon baking soda and water.

    - You do not need to peel the skins off after washing them, but remove stems because they may clog the blades.

    - Apples can be stored at room temperature, but for a longer life span, refrigerate.

    - Juices will last up to fourteen days in an airtight glass mason jar.

- Truth: Restores strength, protects bones, manages diabetes, lowers cholesterol, and prevents kidney, heart, and lung disease.

Basil

- Rinse off dirt. No need to cut; put in juicer whole.

  - Use basil sparingly. This small herb will overpower any fruit or vegetable you pair it with.

- Store in refrigerator.

  - Truth: Great for digestion, depression, diabetes, liver function, and upset stomach.

Beets

- Buy firm beets. Wash, cut top and bottom off, and peel skin off.

- Beets will turn your urine and feces red, so do not be alarmed.

  - Beets have a very strong taste, so if you make sixteen ounces of beet lemonade and would like to taste the lemon in this juice, peel the lemon, and put the whole lemon in to juice, or add an extra half of a lemon for a kick.

  - Store in refrigerator or at room temperature, but after a few days, the beets will get soft at room temperature.

  - Juices will last up to eight days in an airtight glass mason jar.

  - Truth: Lowers blood pressure, boosts endurance and stamina, increases energy levels, reduces birth defects, and promotes brain health.

Cabbage (Red)

- Cut, wash, and use sparingly.

    - Red cabbage is very strong and will take over the taste of any fruit or vegetable you pair it with.

    - Juices will last up to seven days in an airtight glass mason jar.

    - Store in refrigerator or at room temperature.

    - Truth: Promotes eye health and weight loss. Manages ulcers and Alzheimer's disease. Boosts metabolism. Filters the blood. Manages hypertension.

Cantaloupe

- Cantaloupe should feel heavier than it looks and smell musky and sweet when purchasing. Press your thumb in slightly on the bottom and top. There shouldn't be a lip around the stem. The smell of the melon.

- Cut melon in half, take seeds out, and peel skin off. Cut melon to fit in juicer, and juice.

- Store in refrigerator or at room temperature.

- Juices will last up to eight days in an airtight glass mason jar.

    - Truth: Helps with cardiovascular health, lowers metabolic syndrome, reduces stress, helps with menstrual cramps, and prevents wrinkles.

Carrot

- Buy very firm carrots. Cut each end off; scrub or skin carrot.

- Carrots will overpower any juice if you add too many. Proceed with caution.

- Carrots may turn your urine and feces orange, so don't be alarmed.

- Store at room temperature. Carrots will become soft in the refrigerator.

- Juices will last up to eight days in an airtight glass mason jar.

    - Truth: Strengthens vision, improves skin disorders, lowers cholesterol, promotes healthier pregnancy, and can reduce cancer risks.

Celery

- Cut the end off the celery, and then soak in water and 1/2 teaspoon baking soda. Celery will float, while dirt sinks. Rinse and scrub excess dirt off.

- Store celery at room temperature. Once you put celery in the refrigerator, it softens.

- Juice the whole celery once you cut off the end of the celery.

- Crisp, hard celery is the best celery to juice.

    - Juice only will work as an instant laxative with a quart-size mason jar on an empty stomach.

    - Celery juice makes you very gassy; farts will occur.

    - Juices will last up to four days in an airtight glass mason jar.

- The lighter the celery, the sweeter the juice becomes.

- The darker the celery, the more bitter the juice becomes, but it is most powerful when juiced at this state.

- Celery juice works best alone.

- Truth: Heals the gut, purifies the bloodstream, kills eczema, and strengthens bones.

Collard Greens

- Wash in water and 1/2 teaspoon baking soda and juice.

- Store in refrigerator.

- Juices will last up to four days in an airtight glass mason jar.

  - Truth: Removes toxins from the body, maintains blood pressure, moisturizes skin, and gives luster to hair.

Cucumber

- Buy very firm cucumbers.

  - Wash with water and 1/2 teaspoon of baking soda. Do not skin cucumber. Juice entire cucumber.

  - Store in refrigerator.

  - Juices will last up to three days in an airtight glass mason jar.

  - Truth: Promotes weight loss, hydrates skin, detoxes the body, improves sleep, promotes hair growth, and cools the body.

Fennel

- Buy very firm fennel.

  - Wash and juice everything except the leaves. If you do, you will be drinking parts of the leaves.

  - Store in refrigerator or at room temperature.

  - Truth: Fights off sore throat, protects joints, improves anemia, fights bacteria, stimulates breast milk, fights bad breath, and is rich in fiber.

Garlic

- Peel and juice whole bulb.

- It does make the juice.

- Store in refrigerator.

- Juices will last up to nine days in an airtight glass mason jar.

  - Truth: Controls asthma, cures cough and saggy breasts, reduces blood pressure and dementia, and helps detoxify heavy metals in the body.

Grapefruit

- Cut skin and juice.

- Juices will last up to nine days in an airtight glass mason jar.

- Store at room temperature or refrigerator.

- Truth: Promotes appetite control, aids in weight loss, reduces kidney stones, and prevents insulin resistance and diabetes.

Green Pepper

- Buy very firm green peppers.

- Wash with 1/2 teaspoon baking soda and water, and juice everything.

- Store in refrigerator.

- Juices containing peppers can last up to four days.

    - Truth: Aids with asthma, cuts cardiovascular risks dramatically, maintains colon health, and is great for your skin and hair loss.

Habanero Pepper

- When juicing, be careful of the seeds. If touched, do not put fingers near your face, especially your eyes.

- It does make the juice.

- Store in refrigerator or on shelf.

    - Truth: Lowers cholesterol, reduces blood pressure, fights weight gain, and inhibits the growth of cancer.

Honeydew

- Honeydew should feel heavier than it looks and smell musky and sweet when purchasing. Press your thumb in slightly on the bottom and top. There shouldn't be a lip around the stem. The smell of the melon.

- Cut melon in half, take seeds out, and peel skin off. Cut melon to fit in juicer and juice.

- Store in refrigerator or at room temperature.

- Juices will last up to five days in an airtight glass mason jar.

    - Truth: Good for digestion, hypertension, pregnancy, hydration, bones, teeth, skin, eyes, vision, and weight loss.

Jicama

- Peel and juice.

- It does make the juice.

- Juice can last up to seven days in an airtight glass mason jar.

- Store on counter.

    - Truth: Boosts heart health and promotes digestion. Great for gut bacteria. Natural prebiotic that reduces the risk of cancer and aids weight loss.

Kale

- Buy very crisp and green. Yellow means it's going bad.

- Wash with 1/2 teaspoon baking soda and water, and juice everything.

- Store in refrigerator.

- Juice can last up to four days in an airtight glass mason jar.

- Truth: Helps to keep bones strong, improves immune system, fights off infections, reduces heart disease, promotes healthier vision, and improves type 2 diabetes.

Lemons

- Peel or cut skin and juice whole.

- Store in refrigerator or on shelf.

- Juices will last up to fourteen days in an airtight glass mason jar.

  - Truth: Cure throat infections, internal bleeding, fever, colds, and obesity. Cleanse the stomach and is a natural blood purifier.

Mint

- Buy green and crisp. Spearmint is actually more powerful in taste than the average mint.

- Wash and juice everything.

- Store in refrigerator.

  - Truth: Fights off sore throat, acid reflux, irritable bowel syndrome, bloating, and stomach pains.

Orange

- Peel and juice whole. Any orange will do, but Valencia are the best to juice.

- Store on shelf or in refrigerator.

- Juices will last up to ten days in an airtight glass mason jar.

- Truth: Detoxifies the body, increases blood circulation, reduces inflammation, lowers blood pressure, and balances cholesterol.

Parsley

- Buy green and crisp. Juice whole. Curly or flat will do.

- Store on shelf or in refrigerator.

  - Juices will last up to four days in an airtight glass mason jar.

  - Truth: Protects blood vessels, fights diseases, has strong anti-inflammation properties, improves immune systems, and reduces cancer risk.

Parsnips

- Wash, skin, cut off tip, and juice whole.

- Store in refrigerator.

  - Juices will last up to seven days in an airtight glass mason jar.

  - Truth: Great for digestive system and diabetes. Fight infections, strengthen bones, promote liver health, help with blood pressure, and improve cognitive function.

Pear

- Wash with 1/2 teaspoon baking soda and water, and then juice whole.

- Store in refrigerator.

- Avoid mushy pears. Purchase Asian or Shipova to juice.

- Juices will last up to nine days in an airtight glass mason jar.

  - Truth: Packed with antioxidants, aids digestion, controls blood pressure, helps with vision, and lowers inflammation and cholesterol levels.

Persimmon

- Peel or skin and juice whole.

- Store on shelf or in refrigerator.

  - Juices will last up to seven days in an airtight glass mason jar.

  - Truth: Reduces blood pressure, aids in weight loss, and has a large amount of fiber, which aids in a healthy gut.

  - The persimmon is seasonal.

Pineapple

- Cut skin and stem, and then juice whole.

  - When purchasing, flip the pineapple over, and sniff the stem end. If it has no scent, it's not ripe to juice.

  - Store on shelf.

  - Juices will last up to sixteen days in an airtight glass mason jar.

  - Truth: Promotes men's fertility, relieves joint pain, prevents anemia, heals injury, prevents and cures colds, and treats colitis and acid reflux. The juice also changes the smell and taste of the vagina.

Purple Sweet Potato

- Peel and juice whole.

- Store on shelf.

- Juices will last up to nine days in an airtight glass mason jar.

    - Truth: Reduces blood pressure, aids in weight loss, and has a large amount of fiber, which aids in a healthy gut.

- This potato is seasonal.

Red Peppers

- Wash with 1/2 teaspoon baking soda and water, and then juice whole.

- Store in refrigerator.

- Juices will last up to five days in an airtight glass mason jar.

    - Truth: Helps with liver issues, irritable bowel syndrome, and skin care. Adds luster and stimulates hair growth.

Spinach

- Buy crisp, green leaves, and wash with 1/2 teaspoon baking soda and water. Juice whole.

- Store in refrigerator.

- Juices will last up to four days in an airtight glass mason jar.

- Truth: Detoxifies the body, adds luster and shine to hair, hydrates skin, reduces stress, promotes eye health, and helps with kidney stones.

Sweet Potato

- Cut skin and juice.

- Store on shelf.

    - Juices will last up to eight days in an airtight glass mason jar.

    - Truth: Helps with stomach ulcers, blood pressure, fetal development.

Tomato

- Wash with 1/2 teaspoon baking soda and water, and then juice whole. Any tomato will do.

- Store in refrigerator.

- Juices will last up to ten days in an airtight glass mason jar.

    - Truth: Prevents high cholesterol, aids in weight loss, regulates bowel movements, energizes the body, and is great for hair and skin.

Turmeric

- Juice whole and use sparingly. Turmeric overpowers any produce its paired with.

- Store on shelf or refrigerator.

- Juice will last up to twenty days in a glass an airtight glass mason jar, by itself.

  - Truth: Will eliminate all inflammation throughout the body. Supports healthy joints, cardiovascular system, and cholesterol levels. Reduces stress levels. Aids in weight loss, blood-sugar levels, and brain health. Improves mood, soothes digestion, and promotes healthy skin.

Watermelon

- Cut rind, and juice whole. Any watermelon will do, but the sweetest have a large yellowish discolored area.

- Store on shelf or in refrigerator.

- Juices will last up to five days in an airtight glass mason jar.

  - Truth: Aids in weight loss. Works as a natural Viagra by increasing the blood flow to the penis. Lowers inflammation throughout the body, reduces muscle soreness, improves heart health, and keeps you hydrated.

Yellow Pepper

- Wash in 1/2 teaspoon baking soda and water, and juice whole.

- Store on shelf in or refrigerator.

  - Juices will last up to four days in an airtight glass mason jar.

  - Truth: Aids in weight loss, helps keep the skin healthy, gives you energy, fights heart disease, repairs damaged cells and tissues, and has very high amounts of fiber, protein, and iron.

Zucchini

- Wash in 1/2 teaspoon baking soda and water, and juice whole. Buy very firm zucchini.

- Store on shelf or refrigerator.

- Juices will last up to four days in an airtight glass mason jar.

    - Truth: A great source of fiber. Slows down aging, lowers blood sugar levels, supports healthy circulation and healthy heart, improves eye health, and boosts energy, weight loss, thyroid, and adrenal functions.

* The truth statements listed above are real-life responses from myself, my family, my friends, and my juicing clients. Everyone's body is different, and it may or may not work for you. You can not drink one juice and expect to reap the benefits of juicing. Benefits come when you follow instructions suggested in this book.

JUICING FOR A PURPOSE

Throughout my juicing career, I always asked my juice clients:

What are your goals?

Are there any medical issues, that I maybe able to assist with through juicing?

Most of the time, my juice clients' goals are weight loss, and others are medical. Below are some medical issues that some of my juice clients decided to fix through juicing. After telling them I am not a medical doctor and to consult their primary doctor before beginning, if they are clear to juice, I'm here to help.

Acne

While completing a juice cleanse of only two weeks, one of my juice clients reported clearer skin. This wasn't even her goal, but I would throw in a Red Robbin, Celery Juice, or Sexy Tina every now and then. These are a few juices that help with acne.

Blood Pressure

Many juice clients that suffer from high blood pressure chose to juice as an alternative to their prescribed medications, but two stories stick out. Let's start with the positive.

While completing a three-month juice cleanse, this particular juice client had no signs of high blood pressure. Juices like Beet Lemonade, Carrot Plus, Sweet Beet, Parsnip Punch, Nature's Egg-Not, and Sweet Potato Punch helped. He did so well on his juice journey, he even changed his eating habits from meat to fish and finally to a plant-based diet. (The truth is, once you're on a juice cleanse/detox/fast for that long period of time, your body will reject any foods that are not good for the body.) He comes and orders juices sometimes, but he does so well on his own, he rarely gets a juice cleanse.

This second story wasn't so great. While completing a month-long juice cleanse, this juice client experienced a heart attack—in his case, the second one. He survived, but his doctors concluded he was drinking too much vitamin K, and he should not have been drinking any green juices while on blood thinners. I didn't know he was on blood thinners, and we both found out through this horrible experience that drinking green juices while taking blood thinners is a bad thing.

Diabetes

While on a juice cleanse for two weeks, this juice client's lab results changed from one month to the next in a positive way. Using green apples and more vegetable based juices like Celery, oh heck no, Koi, So Cool, and Spicy Orange helped change her levels. Personally, I felt, if she had stayed on the cleanse for longer than two weeks, she could have reversed diabetes through her body for good.

Eczema

While drinking thirty-two ounces of celery juice for breakfast only for a two-week period, I reversed the spread of eczema on my body. I decided to go plant based due to this issue. I still get breakouts, but they only occur when I eat out if there may be a trace of dairy in the food. I knew dairy was the cause of my eczema breakouts after eating yogurt and stopping for a sixty-day period. I completed a juice fast of sixty days, and when I ate the yogurt after the sixty-day fast, I instantly broke out. The eczema hurt and burned so bad, I vowed to never eat dairy again. You can't watch what every cook uses, but whenever a breakout occurs, drink celery straight—and a lot of it. Take a shower, pat the infected area down, use prescribed cream or Vaseline, wrap that infected area in plastic wrap, and go to bed. The area should feel a lot better in the morning. This will not work without the celery juice. Drink 32oz per day for two weeks for the best results.

Erectile Dysfunction

While completing a juice fast of only Beet Lemonade and Watermelon Mojito, I got a phone call from the wife of one of my juice clients. She told me, "Whatever you are giving him, don't stop!" She went on to tell me that they had been having issues with erections for years, and they thought it had to do with his age. She reported they had tried sprays and even Viagra. She said his energy is high, the sex is longer in duration, and he is even carrying her around the room. He purchased a regular juice cleanse for the first five days and got hooked on those two juices. Low and behold, those juices were the cure to the erection issue.

Emphysema

While completing a juice fast of one week, my juice client called to report she can breathe. She is no longer huffing and puffing after walking to her car. After the second week, she reported that she can now climb the steps without having to stop on the second flight of stairs. After the third week, she was in disbelief of what was going on with her. Besides the weight loss, her breathing issues appeared to be under control.

Flu

While on this juice journey of life, I have rarely gotten sick. There was a particular time during the winter months when I felt a little scratch in my throat, a little runny nose, or I was cold. I read that honey, lemon, pineapples, and oranges are the best for colds. Well, since I was plant based, I was not using honey. I tried the lemon, pineapple, and orange and then decided to add turmeric, ginger, and garlic. I knew turmeric pushes the inflammation out of the body, ginger relieves pain and nausea, and people use garlic in socks to reduce fevers, so why not juice it? I combined all those ingredients to make up a sixteen-ounce jar, and I ate eight ounces of sea moss. The sea moss has ninety-two minerals that I must be missing out on, so let me eat that too. Lo and behold, the next morning, I woke up free and clear; all symptoms were gone. So now I call this drink the Winter's Cure. Anyone who requests this juice or mentions they are sick are amazed at how fast their symptoms disappear.

Fertility

I was shocked myself when this happened. I was invited to a health fair in Philadelphia, and this young lady came to me and asked me if I knew of any juices that could helped her get pregnant. I'm big on flushing the system and using turmeric and ginger, and I read somewhere that citrus fruit helped with fertility. I gave her three recipes: Spiced Orange, Grapefruit Mojito, and Koi So Cool. Lo and behold, I get a text stating she was pregnant and she had me to thank. At this point, I'm like, "Oh my goodness, I should have been a doctor." One of my Instagram followers already calls me a juice-ologist, so now I'm sticking with that name from now on. She texted me back to ask me if she can put me in her blog. Her story can be found at victoriouswon1.com. On top of that, she even invited me and her yoga instructor to the baby shower. I was honored. I believe in the power of yoga, so I know that helped, too, along with prayer. Oh, I'm big on prayer.

Gout

I came across a man who went back and forth from New Jersey to Atlanta on business. Whenever he arrived at the airport, he would place his orders in for juices. He always said, "Your juices are the best, no matter where I am in the world." After several orders, he mentioned he had gout. He also mentioned that the reason he orders every time he gets to New Jersey is because he feels so much better after drinking the juices. He follows the cleanse, which includes two juices per day and a meal. He even mentioned that he is able to do yoga, and the juices are working so well that he was purchasing an order for his friend. Well, his friend travels about thirty miles to meet me for juices every other month for two weeks. Juices for gout include Celery, Apple Detox, T. E. Turmeric Toddy, D. Brodie Green, and Jesus Juice.

Irritable Bowel Syndrome

This is where the selling of my juices began! A very dear friend of mine has been experiencing IBS most of her life. I'm not sure how the conversation went, but the next thing I know, she was buying produce and jars, and I started juicing them for her. She juiced for a whole month straight—no food, just water and juice. The first thing I noticed was her skin; she never had pimples or anything, but her skin had this glow. The next thing I noticed was her weight. We met up one day, and she was thin! I was so excited; seeing is believing, and experience is the best teacher. We sat down and talked. She opened up about her IBS, the medications the doctors were giving her, and what was going on with her body. She went on to explain that she had tried everything, and the medications did not work. She stated she felt so much better, better than she had ever felt in her life, and it was because of juicing.

Joint Pain

While working out, this particular juice client would experience joint pain. He never went to the doctors to see what was going on. He said, "I drink water, and I work out. I take vitamins, and nothing seems to be working. Let me try your juices." He would drink his juice before his workout and after his workout. He used to be big on energy drinks and whey smoothies and would drink them before and after a workout. After a week of juicing the way he wanted to do it, he realized he was receiving more energy, his endurance was great, and he didn't experience the joint pain as much as he did before. He continues this juice regimen and rarely talks about joint pain. Juices that help with joint pain are Mean Green, Tropical Green, V. F. Blast, and T. E. Turmeric Toddy, just to name a few.

Liver

After a year of juicing for others, I learned to ask, "Are there any medical issues I can help you with?" To my surprise, this was one of the most important questions of all. This helped me identify what fruits and veggies I can't juice for them and what fruit and veggies work best for them. This juice client was experiencing liver problems; I learned that the liver has trouble breaking down the dye in certain produce. Citrus also helps with the liver. By educating myself, I can help others. He was so impressed with the outcome of juicing, he turned a "let me try this out" to buying juices for two months so far. I gave him juices like Nature's Egg-Not, T. E. Turmeric Toddy, Grapefruit Mojito, Watermelon Mojito, Cucumber Lemonade, Koi and So Cool.

Memory

After juicing for two months, a client would juice for five days straight and take the weekends off. She received a promotion at her job and reported she was able to think more clearly. Another juice client reported the same thing; he reported his memory seem to be better than ever: "The weight loss is a bonus, but I'm getting bonuses at work." They both drank all the juices sent in their juicing plan.

Menstrual Cycle

Whoa! My periods would last seven days, the cramps would last for three days, and my mood would change to evil a week before and the whole week during my period. Juicing changed that. I don't get cramps; my back may hurt for a half a day, and cramps come once in a while, but they only last for a day. I still have bloat—I can't figure out a juice to fix that yet—but the length of days changed to four instead of seven. I still get tired, and I just associate that with losing blood; I can't find a juice for that either. My mood swings don't last for two weeks any more, just the weekend before my period comes on. I hold on to that, because that's my excuse to "tell it like it is," and that's something I rarely do.

Nursing Moms

I have had three nursing moms thus far who reported that while juicing, their milk flow increased. They were pumping twice the amount of milk during the juicing. One father even noticed how much energy their baby had while the mom was juicing. He said, "Come here. Look how happy she is. She must know you are the juice lady." One mom noticed how clear the baby's face became. I told her prior to juicing to stop all dairy products, especially while juicing. Dairy clogs up the arteries. She listened, and the baby's skin and sleeping patterns had changed. She reported that her baby is sleeping through the night. With nursing moms, they do need to eat, but not heavy meals, and refrain from produce they may be allergic to. Strawberries are something I stay away from when giving nursing moms juice, but I will gave them Papaya Mojitos (recipe coming in the next book), Cucumber Mojitos, Carrot Plus, Parsnip Punch, Golden Punch, and Lin-Ale, just to name a few.

Obesity

While I was juicing for others and instructing them on the proper way to lose weight through juicing, my dear mom mentioned something that hit home. She stated, "How can you be the spokesperson for a juicing company, and you don't even look like you juice yourself?" She was right! I was close to two hundred pounds; I loved wine and sweets. My brother Rashaan Waples would say, "You preach a healthy lifestyle but drink wine." He was right! Alcohol adds unwanted pounds and it also impairs your judgement.

I would juice halfway, drink my wine, drink my coffee, eat sweets, and eat bread and fish. On October 2019, I decide to do a fast. I juiced only for thirty days. I had done this before in 2014, but it was different this time. This time, I lost weight, and when I went back to try seafood, because I stop eating meat a long time ago, it didn't agree with my body. Fasting for thirty days allowed me to now be in tune with my body. I started listening to my body. If whatever I put in my body made my stomach bloated, I instantly stopped and didn't pick that particular food up again. If my stomach hurt after eating, I was not eating that food either. If my finger broke out with eczema, that meant it was something I ate that contained dairy. If my face broke out (and my face never breaks out), I definitely was not touching that food. I finally lost the weight, I started to look like my juice clients, and I love who I have become. I don't eat when I'm bored. I don't believe you have to eat three square meals a day, and when I am full, I am full. I mastered obesity through fasting and prayer, because if it wasn't for the Lord, I would have quit on October 3.

Stress

Seven out of ten juice clients report mood changes, in a very good way. Pineapple helps with that; pineapple is a happy fruit, and when my juice clients purchase a juice plan, one of the main ingredients in about three of their juices is pineapple. Pineapple not only creates a good smell in the vaginal area, but it also makes you feel good.

HOW LATOYA BECAME PREGNANT WITH BABY HALO

Written by Latoya, November 2019. This story can be found on Latoya's blog at victoriouswon1.com.

A day before my juice cleanse I came across this woman named Yara, who had a mobile juice business called Juice Capitol. Yara sold her juices at a community gardening event my partners and I went to, to plant seeds for the upcoming fall. My partner noticed Yara selling the juices first and told her about me, then sent me back to speak with her. I was excited because everything was flowing in divine order.

When I went back to speak with Yara, she had a juice called Starburst that called my name. The ingredients had all of the colors I was focusing on and it was delicious. I told Yara I was doing a fertility cleanse. She got excited and immediately wanted to give me her information because she just wrote a book on the many juices and the newest one was specifically for fertility cleansing. I supported her delicious business and she gave me a few of the ingredients for the cleanse and I purchased the fruits right away!

The fertility ingredients are

- Spiced Orange: Orange, turmeric and ginger
- Grapefruit Mojito: grapefruit, mint, key lime and apple
- Citrus Blast: grapefruit, orange, apple, lime, lemon and ginger

HOW PETE'S BLOOD PRESSURE BECAME CONTROLLED BY JUICING

For the last 30 days, I have been doing the juicing done by Yara Waples. After almost 30 days, I started out at almost 222 and I am now down to 202. My blood pressure is great: 120/70. I went to the doctors and the doctors gave me the absolute clean bill of health. I just like to say after 30 days, it really works for me. I juice twice a day, 5 days a week. Weekends I am moderate. I eat sensible, drink plenty water, 30 mins of work out and only 3 times a week. Nothing big, nothing drastic, but I will give her an outstanding reference to the product that she puts out. I am telling all my friends and Facebook family to give her a chance, give her a shot, Yara Juice is what it's all about. Thank you Yara! (Singing) I am ready for the summer.

—recorded by Pete Brown on Facebook, May 2018

How Leon's Liver Improved after Juicing

Mr. Leon has been juicing with me since the end of November 2019. When he first called me, he reported his liver has been failing, and someone told him to call. At this point, he was at 30 percent liver failure; he weighed 280 pounds and reported high blood pressure.

On February 19, 2020, I get a call from Mr. Leon:

Mr. Leon: Hello?

Me: Hey, Mr. Leon! How are you?

Mr. Leon: I just wanted to call and thank you! I went to the doctors and my liver is now functioning at 47 percent, I lost thirty pounds, and my blood pressure levels are stable. The doctor told me to keep up the good work and whatever you are doing, please keep it up.

Me: Oh my goodness, I am so very happy for you. God is so good.

Mr. Leon: Yes, he is, and I will be calling you for my next juice cleanse Friday.

*Juicing picture taken in December 2019

*Phone conversation February 2020

HOW JUICING BECAME A LIFESTYLE FOR YARA

In May 2019, a very good friend of mine, Sylvia Saunders, sent me a picture of me sitting at a party. I zoomed in on that picture and noticed how big I really was. By this time, I had tried Herbal life, the Cookie Diet, the South Beach Diet, diet pills, and the Water Diet, and I even went raw for six weeks after giving birth to my son, Koi. I would lose weight and regain it back, and after eleven years, I still had my baby weight. By this time, my son was eleven years old. I would juice, fast, and cheat by eating cakes, meat, and cheese and drinking wine. My mom would say, "You need to be a walking poster board for your business, and you don't look like it. You promote health and drink wine, then cheat on the very same plan you tell others to follow." That stuck, so I started another juice cleanse and decided to do a juice fast in October 2019. I didn't get on the scale because I believe you can't be measured, and your clothes will tell you how well you are doing. The clothes did; they began to get to big. Today, I am the walking billboard of Juice Capitol. My brother showed me an exercise with a deck of cards that I really enjoy. So I am on my way to my prebaby weight, ha. Now I juice every day, sometimes twice a day, and I am vegan. If I decide to have a vegan snack, I do, but I don't overeat. I listen to my body. If the food I consume hurts my stomach, I won't eat it again.

MYTHS ABOUT JUICING

- You can store your juice in any type of container. *Glass is the safest for your body.*

- You should only drink cold-press juices. *Shake the separation up, and drink.*

- You can open a juice and save it for later. *Juices needs to be consumed within two hours.*

- You don't need to consult your doctor. *Taking certain meds and juicing can kill you.*

- You can eat before juicing. *Juicing should be done on an empty stomach.*

- You can still take vitamins and juice. *The main sources of vitamins are juiced in your jar.*

- You need protein. *Protein is found in all your greens. Drink what cows eat: protein!*

- There is only one way to juice. *You can fast or drink a juice twice a day or once a day.*

- You cannot work out and juice fast. *Juicing will give you more energy than food.*

- You can juice with shelf-bought juices. *Shelf-bought juices are not real juice.*

- You can only drink juices if you are near a toilet. *You should have a steady, easy flow.*

A masticating juicer is a better juicer: if you are incorporate juicing as your new way of living, any juicer will do. You will not lose minerals or vitamins, if you choose to buy a centrifugal juicer. The only difference is you use less produce with a masticating juicer. The masticating juicer is very slow, where the centrifugal juicer is fast. It creates heat near the blade. Bottom line is, if you follow instructions the proper way, you will reap the benefits from juicing daily, no matter which machine you decide to use.

Golden Punch:

Golden beet, pineapple, turmeric, ginger, apple and carrot

Benefits include aiding weight loss, boost longevity, sex, Natural Anti-Inflammatory Compound. Increases the Antioxidant Capacity of the Body. Boosts Brain-Derived Neurotrophic Factor, Linked to Improved Brain Function and a Lower Risk of Brain Diseases.

@juicing_is_life

JUICE CAPITOL

Starburst

Pineapples, Yellow pepper, ginger, apple
Benefits include eye health like visual impairments including macular degeneration and cataracts, the main causes of which are old age and infections.

@juicing_is_life

Father RT

Kale, collard greens, parsley, spinach

Benefits include natural diuretic, which helps to eliminate excess fluid without depleting the body of potassium. This juice helps to eliminate excess fluid without depleting the body of potassium. This juice is also an excellent source of vitamin A, vitamin C, and calcium, a rich source of vitamin K, and a good source of iron, vitamin B-6, and magnesium.

Purple Haze

Purple Sweet Potato, pineapple, apple, lemon, lime, ginger

Benefits include great endurance for athletes and ultra runners. Helps to lower and regulate blood pressure, helpful in managing diabetes, gout, inflammation and prevents blood clots. Aids in weight loss, cancer fighting and purple sweet potato root has antibacterial properties that destroys bacteria or suppresses their growth or their ability to reproduce with *E. coli, Salmonella, Proteus, and Vibrio parahaemolyticus.*

www.juicecapitol.co

Bev Juice

Pineapple, carrot, ginger, turmeric

People include strengthen your immune system and help your body fight off infections, add this juice to your daily diet and maintain your physical health. This juice contains antioxidants, which help your body fight free radicals, cell damage, and inflammation.

@juicing_is_life

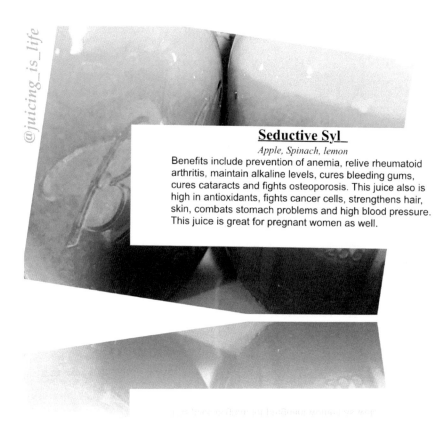

Seductive Syl

Apple, Spinach, lemon

Benefits include prevention of anemia, relive rheumatoid arthritis, maintain alkaline levels, cures bleeding gums, cures cataracts and fights osteoporosis. This juice also is high in antioxidants, fights cancer cells, strengthens hair, skin, combats stomach problems and high blood pressure. This juice is great for pregnant women as well.

Sweet Tart

Rhubarb
Strawberry
Apple

www.juicecapitol.com

JOURNAL YOUR THIRTY-DAY JUICE JOURNEY

I challenge you to a thirty-day juice challenge! You have two options: drink three juices (sixteen ounces per meal), or drink two juices (sixteen ounces for breakfast and lunch) and eat vegetables only. You can drink water, sea moss, and herbal tea (I suggest dandelion tea, because it helps curb your appetite, but choose what you like). Write down how you feel, what you accomplished each day, how much water you drank, your weight loss, mood, exercise, bowel movements (color, size, and how many per day), skin tone, sex drive, sleep patterns, and any setbacks. Listen, we all have setbacks, so if you fall off one day, get back on the wagon and continue. Having a journal will also help with the next time you complete a juice challenge.

Example : Day 5: Drank 3 juices/60 oz water/30 min walk/8 hrs sleep/BM: 3X long lean, red/happy, energy 100%/bloat went away, lose 5 pounds/I can breathe/my skin is clearing, etc.

Example : Day 5: Drank 3 juices/60 oz water/30 min walk/8 hrs sleep/BM: 3X long lean, red/happy, energy 100%/bloat went away, lose 5 pounds/I can breathe/my skin is clearing, etc.

Example : Day 5: Drank 3 juices/60 oz water/30 min walk/8 hrs sleep/BM: 3X long lean, red/happy, energy 100%/bloat went away, lose 5 pounds/I can breathe/my skin is clearing, etc.

Example : Day 5: Drank 3 juices/60 oz water/30 min walk/8 hrs sleep/BM: 3X long lean, red/happy, energy 100%/bloat went away, lose 5 pounds/I can breathe/my skin is clearing, etc.

Example : Day 5: Drank 3 juices/60 oz water/30 min walk/8 hrs sleep/BM: 3X long lean, red/happy, energy 100%/bloat went away, lose 5 pounds/I can breathe/my skin is clearing, etc.

Example : Day 5: Drank 3 juices/60 oz water/30 min walk/8 hrs sleep/BM: 3X long lean, red/happy, energy 100%/bloat went away, lose 5 pounds/I can breathe/my skin is clearing, etc.

Example : Day 5: Drank 3 juices/60 oz water/30 min walk/8 hrs sleep/BM: 3X long lean, red/happy, energy 100%/bloat went away, lose 5 pounds/I can breathe/my skin is clearing, etc.

Example : Day 5: Drank 3 juices/60 oz water/30 min walk/8 hrs sleep/BM: 3X long lean, red/happy, energy 100%/bloat went away, lose 5 pounds/I can breathe/my skin is clearing, etc.

Example : Day 5: Drank 3 juices/60 oz water/30 min walk/8 hrs sleep/BM: 3X long lean, red/happy, energy 100%/bloat went away, lose 5 pounds/I can breathe/my skin is clearing, etc.

Example : Day 5: Drank 3 juices/60 oz water/30 min walk/8 hrs sleep/BM: 3X long lean, red/happy, energy 100%/bloat went away, lose 5 pounds/I can breathe/my skin is clearing, etc.

Example : Day 5: Drank 3 juices/60 oz water/30 min walk/8 hrs sleep/BM: 3X long lean, red/happy, energy 100%/bloat went away, lose 5 pounds/I can breathe/my skin is clearing, etc.

ABOUT THE AUTHOR

Kashana "Yara" Waples, MBA

Kashana "Yara" Waples was born and raised in the city of Camden. She attended Forrest Hill and Hatch Middle School and graduated from Camden High
School in 1998. After high school, she attended Rowan University, where she received her bachelor's in psychology. Four years later, she received her MBA from
Eastern University. She has completed various training courses, including the Six
Sigma Green Belt program from Rutgers/Lockheed Martin, behavioral health
training from Rutgers University, and CADC training. She is a lifetime member
of the NAACP, since the age of ten.

In the early part of Waples's career, she worked at Kennedy Hospital as a mental health tech for eight years, drug and alcohol counselor at Garden State Youth Correctional Facility, and behavioral analyst for Apple Counseling. After receiving her MBA, she was hired as a program manager for Devereux of New Jersey, where she oversaw seven group homes and opened up two sex-offender group homes in the Woodbine, New Jersey, area.

Waples started a small business under Waples Consulting Firm, working with Camden Repertory Theater as a marketing director, Roof Top Grill as a marketing director, and various small businesses as a consulting manager from Camden to Philadelphia. This included business planning, advising on steps to obtain business credit, website building, designing flyers and business cards, and managing social media. Currently, she is involved with building her brand through her juicing company, Juice Capitol.

She is the granddaughter of the late Gretchen Waples, who owned the Waples Funeral Home in Camden, New Jersey, before her death in 2012. She is a single mother to a handsome son named Koi Peeples. She is the daughter of the most loving supportive mother on planet earth, Linda Jackson and the late Artie Waples Jr. Her siblings include Robbin Pegues, Robert Pegues, and Rashann Waples.

Made in the USA
Middletown, DE
26 June 2020